> CONT

✔ KU-363-448

>>>>
ENTER

EMMI /MARTIAL ARTS

Born into a world of rising threat —

— they witnessed terror strike the safety of their town.

As they grew up, each member developed a unique ability . . .

FORENSICS

MARTIAL ARTS

COMPUTERS

GADGETRY

In the corridors of Seaside High, the four of them united.

They combined their skills and formed the most high-tech and secret security force on Earth.

RECON ACADEMY

CONTINUE >>>>

5

SECTION

1

ACCESS GRANTED 〉〉〉〉

EMMI
MARTIAL ARTS

128718
293829
9283
98289
89
1
109201
192091
1992

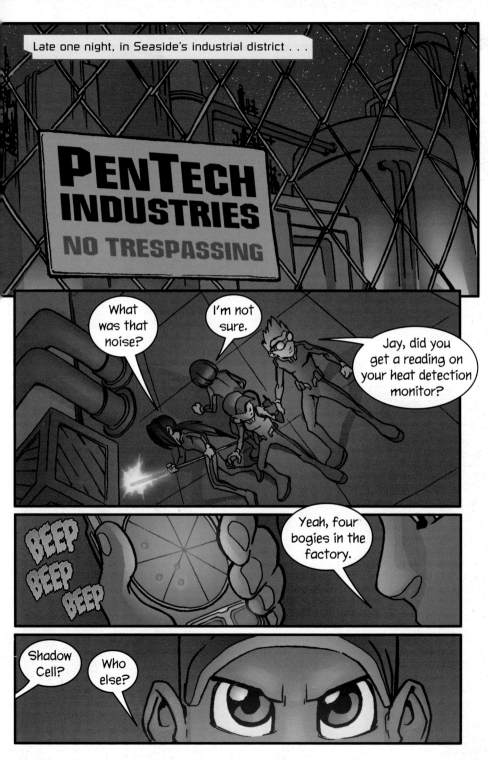

11

SECTION

FILE NO.
1437578

2

ACCESS GRANTED >>>>

EMMI
MARTIAL ARTS

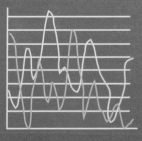

128718
293829
9283
98289
89
1
109201
192091
1992

Moments later, at Emmi's house . . .

Make it quick, Jay! I'm playing an awesome new game.

RRRRRINNG!

Me too! I just got this cool laptop!

New laptop? What kind?

21

SECTION

ACCESS GRANTED 〉〉〉〉

EMMI
MARTIAL ARTS

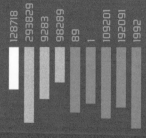

8579
1564574
109201
192091
1992
745979

128718
293829
9283
98289
69
1
109201
192091
1992

Soon . . .

Come on!

I know a shortcut!

Look! Up ahead!

29

Now for my dismount!

BOING!

FWIP FWIP FWIP

Whoa!

Where's Jay?

SECTION 4

W EWUWS EWEMGH EJMEFE WMEGHE EJH9DFH
E4J99FX F4SF94FD F49FKLWMFLSDKPDQKRG
KRG UJ9FJ 94FMWJF JDFJWLF J 4MMFD4FDLWF WI.
WMFDK4F WMFFKID4MF4KPDK4 F4LFK(4K 94JNWK
JWEJF 9WJFWEJF WFMJWSFHGJBBFN99F4F 4FN9
W9FSHJ89SGHVNE9SGHESEEEM EEGUSG GER2J
RGUS9 JRG KEGJJDEDRJ9SBJ 4J99F2B2J Q2RGM
RGJS9SJ89SMG EERGLMI QERGME9SGDMRGMRKD S
R QRGDDGD9GLKRGLKDLRQK ZRGKDQKRGKRG
94J99FX F4SF94FD F49FKLWMFLSDKPDQKRG
F9J49FJ 84FMWJF JDFJWLF J 4MMFD4FDLWF WI
FDK4F WMFFKID4MF4KPDK4 F4LFK(4K94JNWK
WEJF 9WJFWEJF WFMJWSFHGJBB 984F 4FN9
W9FSHJ89SGHVNE9SGHE9EEEM EEGUSG GER2J
RJDJ9 JRG FE9 JJDEDRJ9SBJ 8J99F2B2J Q2RGM
RGJS9SJ89SMG EERGLMI QERGME9SGDMRGMRKD S
R QRGDDGD9GLKRGLKDLRQK ZRGKDQKRGKRG
94J99FX F4SF94FD F49FK WMFLSDKPDQKRG
F9J49FJ 84FMWJF JDFJWLF J 4MFD4FDLWF WI
FDK4F WMFFKID4MF4KFDK4 F4LFKI4K94JNWK
WEJF 9WJFWEJF WFMJWSFHGJBFN94F 4FN9
W9FSHJ89SGHVNE9SGHE9EEEM EEGUSG GER2J
RJDJ9 JRG KEGJJDEDRJ9SBJ 4J99J9BJ Q2RGM
JS9SJ89SMG EERGLMI QERGME9SGDMRGMRKD S
R QRGDDGD9GLKRGLKDLRQK ZRGKDQKRGKRG
94J99FX F4SF94FD F49FKLWMFLSDKPDQKRG
F9J49FJ 84FMWJF JDFJWLF J 4MMFD4FDLWF WI
FDK4F WMFFKID4MF4KFDK4 F4LFK(4K94JNWK
WEJF 9WJFWEJF WFM
W9FSHJ89SGHVNE9

ACCESS GRANTED)))

EMMI
MARTIAL ARTS

128718
293829
9283
98289
89
1
109201
192091
1992

1827178   198291821   918298

1827178   198291821   918298

Soon . . .

They couldn't have gone far.

Wait! I'm picking up an image from one of our remote cameras.

Hey! I recognize that van!

It's Shadow Cell. They're heading into Thorton Woods.

That's a secure area.

Not anymore.

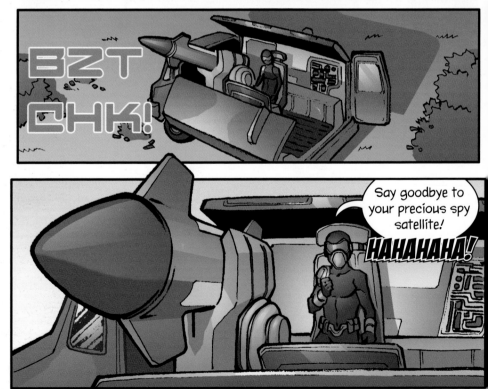

SECTION

FILE NO. 1437578

5

ACCESS GRANTED >>>>

EMMI
MARTIAL ARTS

128718
293829
9283
98289
89
1
109201
192091
1992

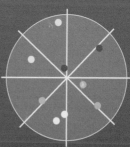

SPYSPACE

a place for international spies

PROFILE

NAME: Emilia Rodriguez

CODE NAME: Emmi

AGE: 14

HEIGHT: 1.6 metres

WEIGHT: 51 kilograms

EYES: brown

HAIR: brown

SPY ORG: Recon Academy

SPECIAL ABILITIES: Martial arts expert, gymnast and all around great athlete (not to brag, of course)

FAVOURITES: My specialized bo staff to take down enemies and perform a load of stunts

QUOTE: "You have to believe in yourself." – Sun Tzu

PHOTOS

FRIENDS

Ryker   Haz   Jay   004

BLOG
recent posts   see all

 Hey, guys! Just updated my pics and wanted to let you know that I'm back online!

 Welcome back to cyberspace, Em. So, you must have got a new laptop.

 I wish :(I'm typing this message from the school library. I don't think my grandma will ever let another laptop in the house, not after what happened yesterday.

 Tell me about it. My dad got so freaked, he even threw out our microwave! Plus, I'm grounded for two weeks...like blowin' up the kitchen was my fault.

 Bummer.

 btw, glad you guys decided to watch the launch with me. Told you it'd be totally worth it.

 Yeah, like we had a choice ;)

) CASE FILE

CASE: "Shadow Cell Scam"
CASE NUMBER: 9781474784306
AGENT: Emmi
ORGANIZATION: Recon Academy

SUSPECT: PenTech Industries

OVERVIEW: This small division of the Shadow Cell gang makes their living as highly skilled con artists. Even the most respected agents have been fooled by their deadly trickery and get-rich-quick schemes. Be on the lookout for men with fake moustaches and terrible disguises.

CRIMINAL RECORD:
fraud
grand theft
identity theft
armed robbery

INTELLIGENCE:

anonymity state of being unidentifiable (unknown to others)

scam trick or a lie meant to fool someone else

scheme secret or devious plan used to take advantage of the innocent

HISTORY:

Con artists (confidence men and women) rely on trust and deception to trick innocent people out of their money or possessions.

The phrase "confidence man" was first used in reference to William Thompson in 1849. Thompson went up to strangers on the street and struck up conversations with them. When he felt he had gained their trust (confidence) he would ask to see the person's watch for a moment. After the valuable was in his hand, he would simply walk away without returning the item.

- Other names for a confidence trick: grift, scam, scheme and swindle

- The person targeted by a con man is called a mark.

- A con man's helpers are called shills.

CONCLUSION:

In the modern world, con artists use cyberspace to scam others out of their hard-earned cash by abusing the anonymity offered by the internet. Only the Recon Academy can safeguard us from these digital cons.

> ABOUT THE AUTHOR

Chris Everheart always dreamed of interesting places, fascinating people and exciting adventures. He is still a dreamer. He enjoys writing thrilling stories about young heroes who live in a world that doesn't always understand them. Chris lives in Minnesota, USA, with his family. He plans to travel to every continent on Earth, see interesting places, meet fascinating people and have exciting adventures.

> ABOUT THE ILLUSTRATOR

Arcana Studios, Inc. was founded by Sean O'Reilly in British Columbia, Canada, in 2004. Arcana has since established itself as Canada's largest comic book and graphic novel publisher. A nomination for a Harvey Award and winning the "Schuster Award for Top Publisher" are just a couple of Arcana's accolades. The studio is known as a quality publisher for independent comic books and graphic novels.

) GLOSSARY

bogies unidentified enemies

booted process of starting or restarting a computer

decrypt decode or decipher

detection act of finding something

diversion attempt to distract the enemy

hack gain access to computer information illegally

network computers that are connected so they can work together

prototype first version of an invention that tests an idea to see if it will work

) DISCUSSION QUESTIONS

1. Each member of Recon Academy has a special skill. Which character's skill do you think is most important when it comes to stopping Shadow Cell's evil schemes? Why?

2. If your friend was trapped in a burning building, what would you do first? What would be the safest way of handling the situation? If Jay hadn't had those micro air filters, should they still have gone inside by themselves?

3. Which one of the Recon team members do you like the most? Why?

) WRITING PROMPTS

1. Emmi uses her martial arts and gymnastics skills to fight crime. Make a list of examples where Emmi uses her special skills to get out of sticky situations.

2. On page 11, Hazmat discovers that Shadow Cell has stolen some laptops. What was Shadow Cell planning to do with them? Describe their evil plan.

3. Pretend you're the newest member of Recon Academy. Draw a picture of yourself as a character. Underneath your picture, list a few of your special skills and how they would help the team.

CHECK OUT MORE

ACTION AND ADVENTURE!

> THE HIDDEN FACE OF FREN-Z

> NUCLEAR DISTRACTION

> PREP SQUADRON